PART 1
Oboe
CHAMPAGNE VARIATIONS
from String Sonata #3
G. Rossini
(1792-1868)
Arranged by David Marlatt
Allegro Moderato = 112
Lightly = 132
AF273056
© 2019 EIGHTH NOTE PUBLICATIONS
www.enpmusic.com

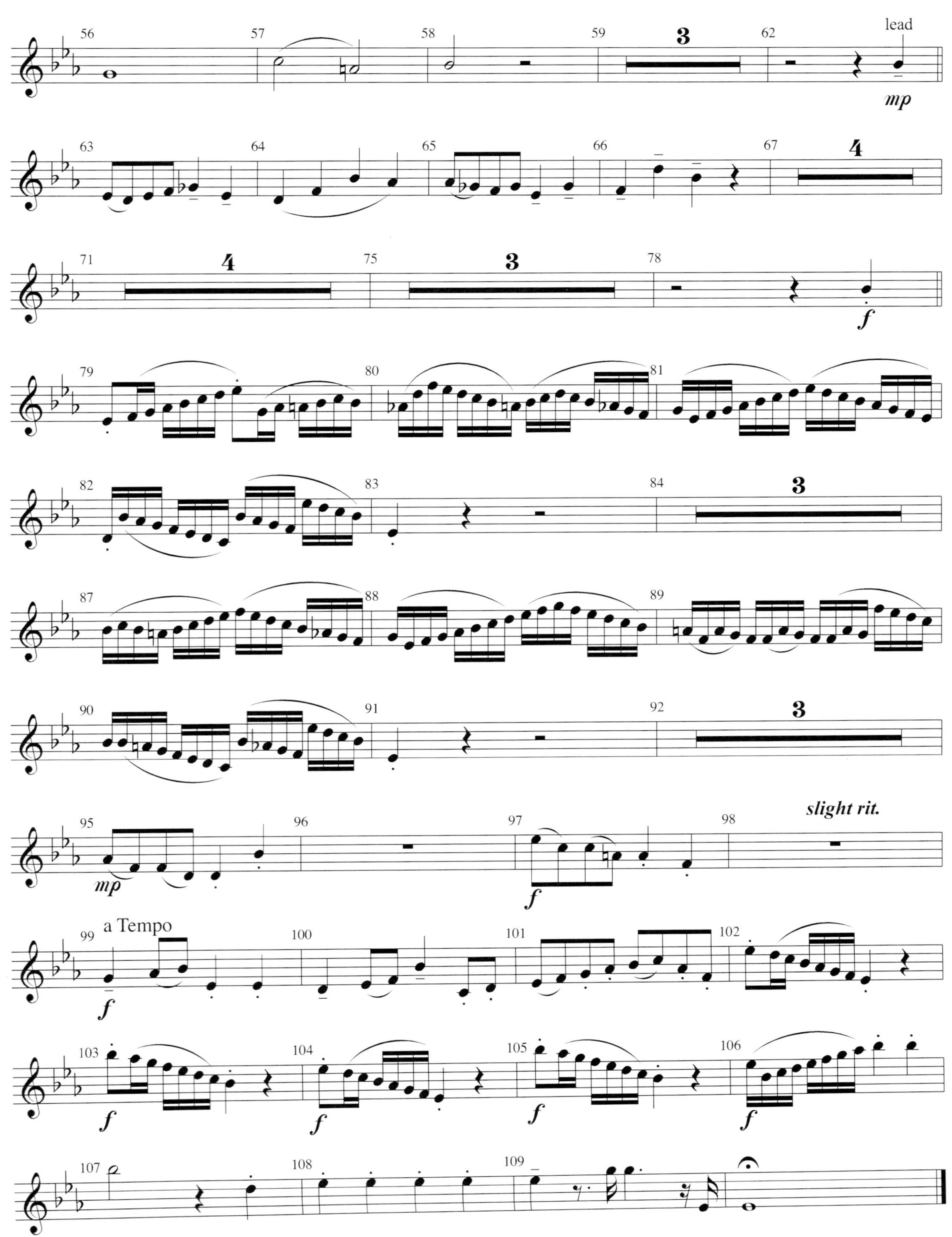

lead
mp
f
slight rit.
a Tempo
mp
f
f
f
f
f
f
CHAMPAGNE VARIATIONS pg. 2

CHAMPAGNE VARIATIONS
from String Sonata #3

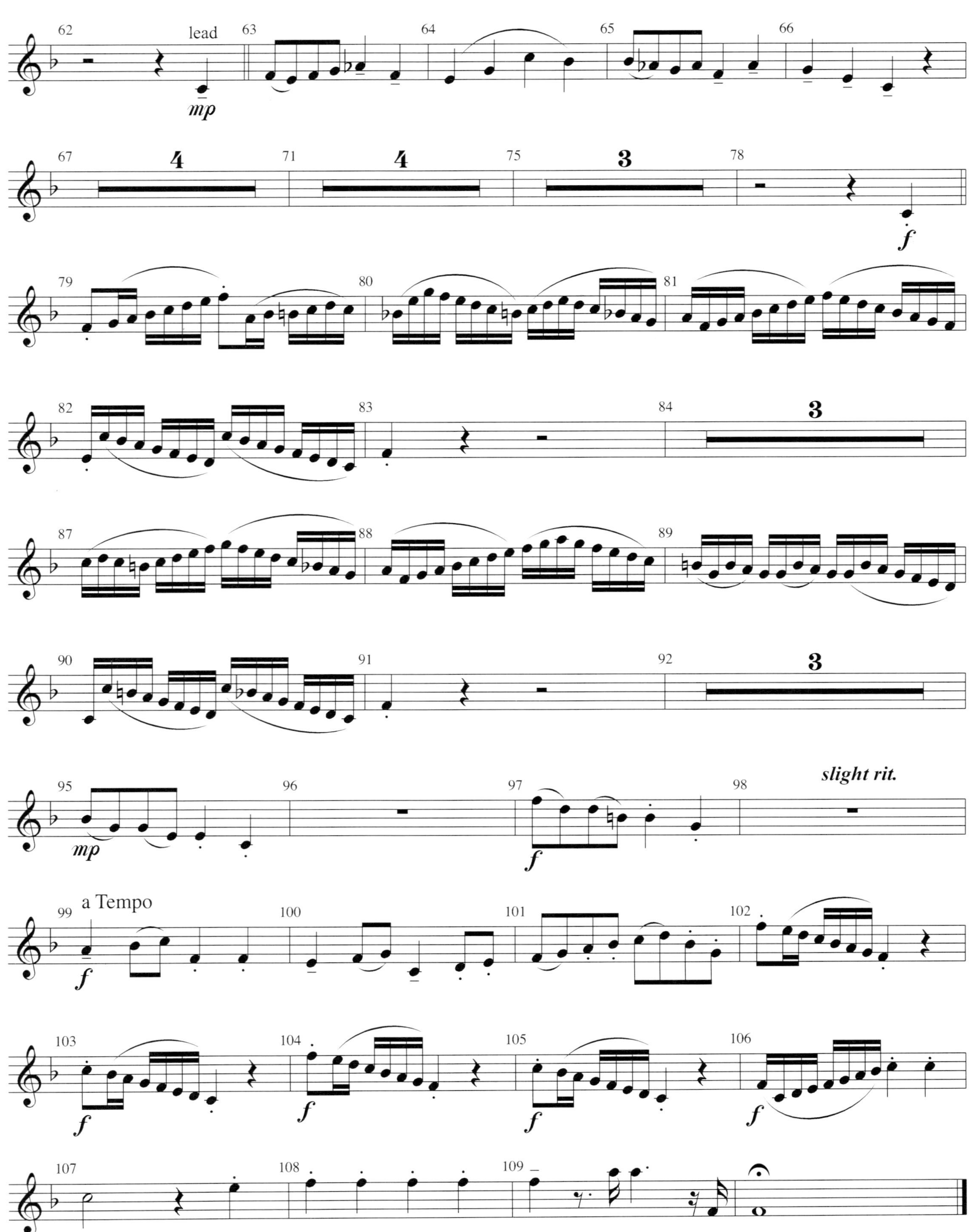

lead
mp
f
slight rit.
mp
f
a Tempo
f
f
f
f
f
CHAMPAGNE VARIATIONS pg. 2

CHAMPAGNE VARIATIONS pg. 2

CHAMPAGNE VARIATIONS

from String Sonata #3

PART 2
Flute

G. Rossini
(1792-1868)
Arranged by David Marlatt

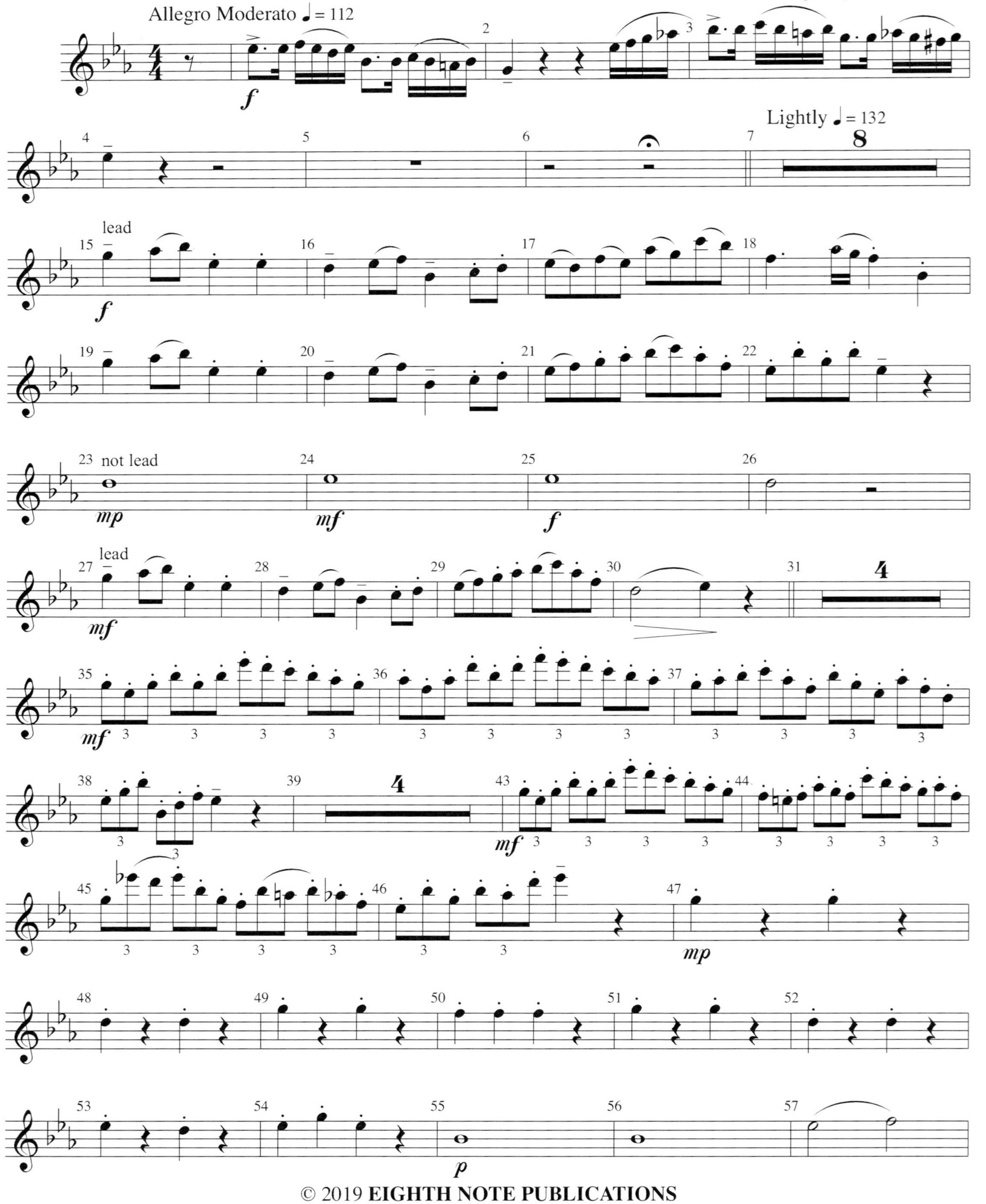

CHAMPAGNE VARIATIONS pg. 4

CHAMPAGNE VARIATIONS
from String Sonata #3

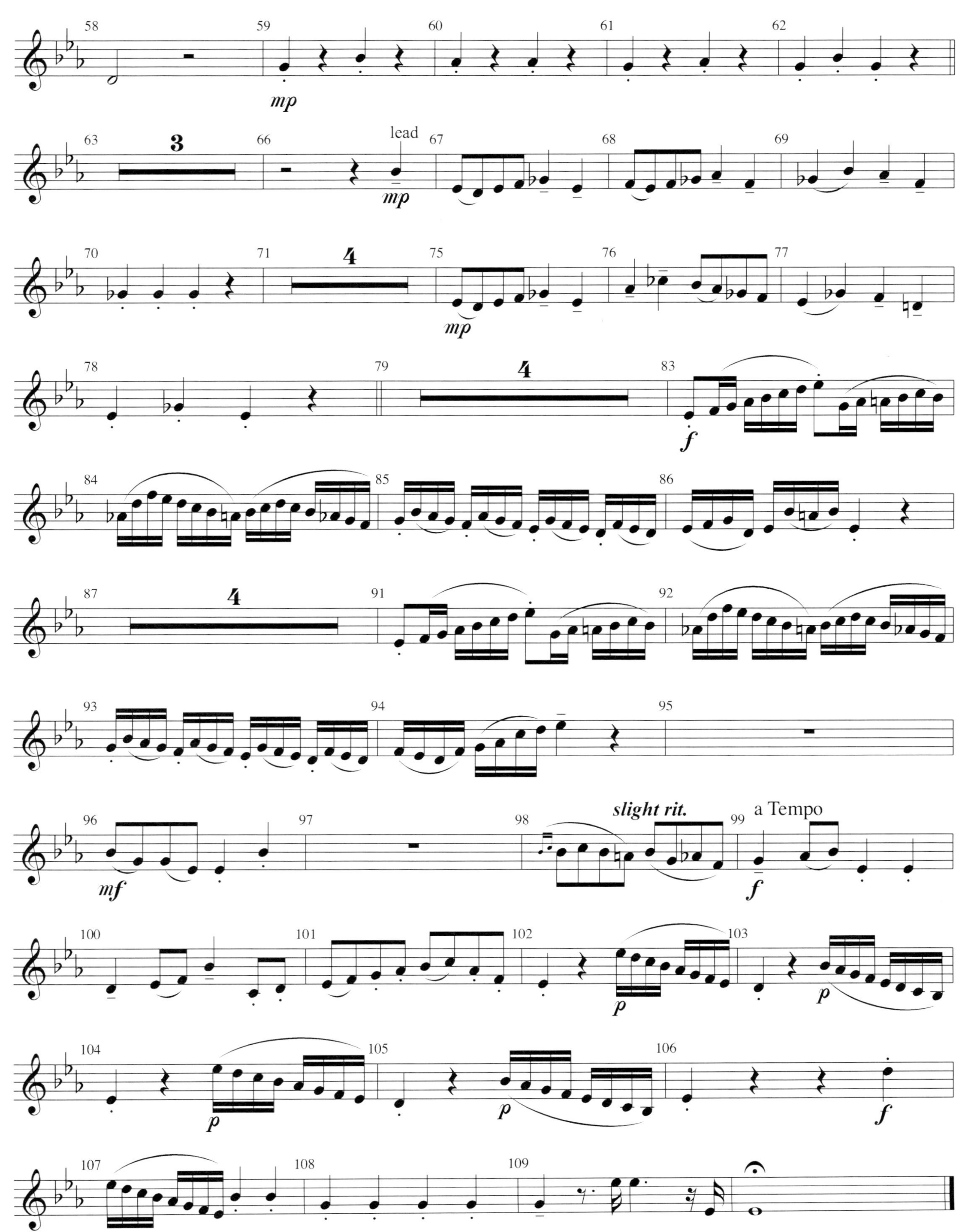

CHAMPAGNE VARIATIONS pg. 2

CHAMPAGNE VARIATIONS
from String Sonata #3

PART 2
B♭ Clarinet

G. Rossini
(1792-1868)
Arranged by David Marlatt

CHAMPAGNE VARIATIONS pg. 2

CHAMPAGNE VARIATIONS pg. 2

CHAMPAGNE VARIATIONS
from String Sonata #3

CHAMPAGNE VARIATIONS
from String Sonata #3

© 2019 **EIGHTH NOTE PUBLICATIONS**
www.enpmusic.com

p
mp
lead
mf
not lead
p
mf
mf
mp
mf
f
slight rit.
a Tempo
f
p
f
p
f
p
f
p
f
CHAMPAGNE VARIATIONS pg. 2

CHAMPAGNE VARIATIONS
from String Sonata #3

© 2019 **EIGHTH NOTE PUBLICATIONS**
www.enpmusic.com

p
mp
lead
mf
73
74
75 not lead
76
mf
slight rit.
a Tempo
f
f
f
mp
mf
p   f   p   f   p   f   p   f
CHAMPAGNE VARIATIONS pg. 2

CHAMPAGNE VARIATIONS
from String Sonata #3
PART 4
B♭ Clarinet
G. Rossini
(1792-1868)
Arranged by David Marlatt
Allegro Moderato ♩ = 112
Lightly ♩ = 132
© 2019 EIGHTH NOTE PUBLICATIONS
www.enpmusic.com

slight rit.
a Tempo
CHAMPAGNE VARIATIONS pg. 2

CHAMPAGNE VARIATIONS
from String Sonata #3
PART 4
Bb Tenor Saxophone
G. Rossini
(1792-1868)
Arranged by David Marlatt 
Allegro Moderato = 112
Lightly = 132
© 2019 EIGHTH NOTE PUBLICATIONS
www.enpmusic.com

CHAMPAGNE VARIATIONS pg. 2

CHAMPAGNE VARIATIONS
from String Sonata #3

© 2019 EIGHTH NOTE PUBLICATIONS
www.enpmusic.com

CHAMPAGNE VARIATIONS pg. 2

CHAMPAGNE VARIATIONS
from String Sonata #3

PART 5
B♭ Bass Clarinet

G. Rossini
(1792-1868)
Arranged by David Marlatt

© 2019 EIGHTH NOTE PUBLICATIONS
www.enpmusic.com

CHAMPAGNE VARIATIONS pg. 2

CHAMPAGNE VARIATIONS

from String Sonata #3

PART 5
E♭ Baritone Saxophone

G. Rossini
(1792-1868)
Arranged by David Marlatt

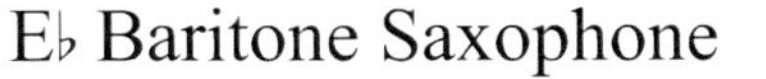

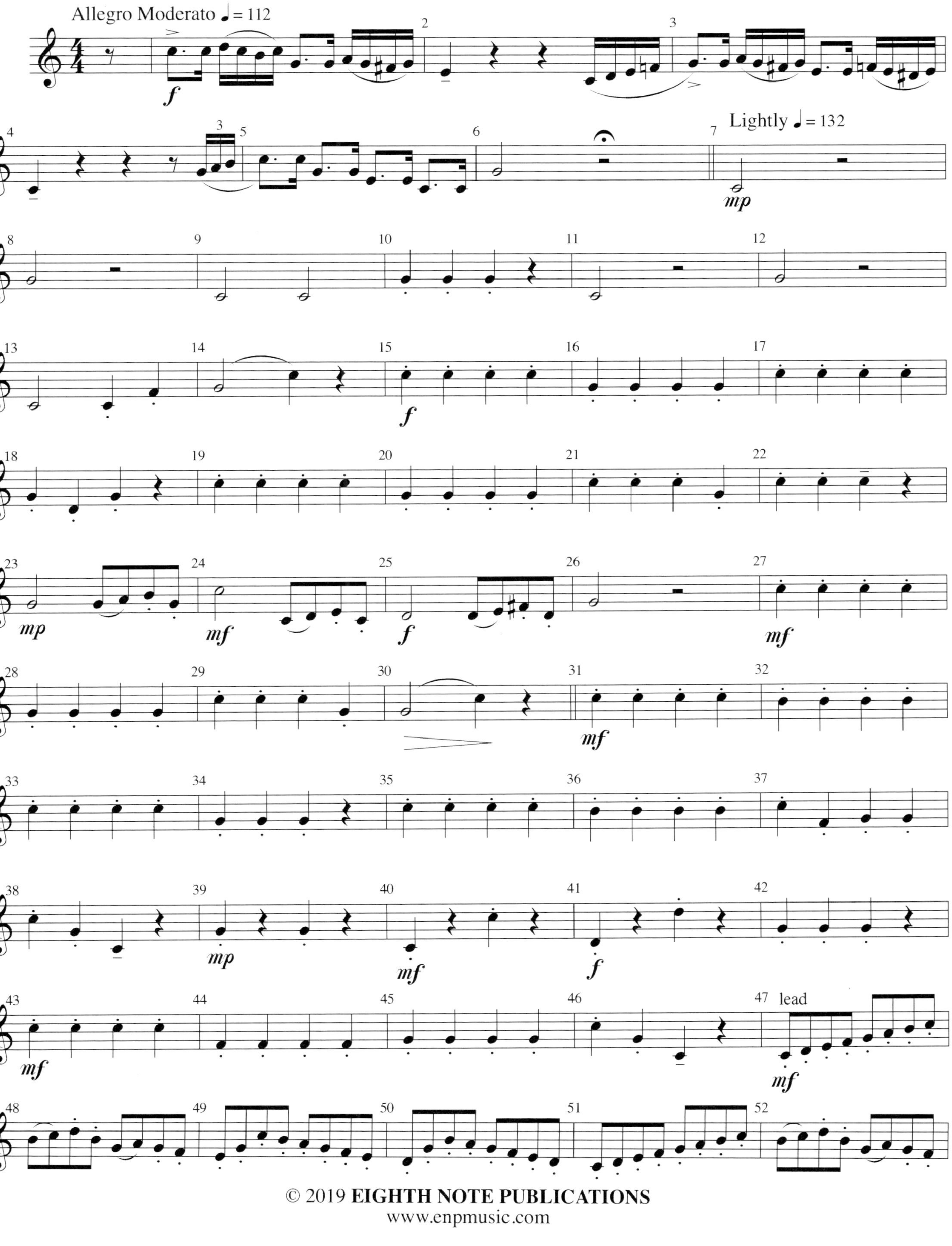

CHAMPAGNE VARIATIONS pg. 2

CHAMPAGNE VARIATIONS
from String Sonata #3

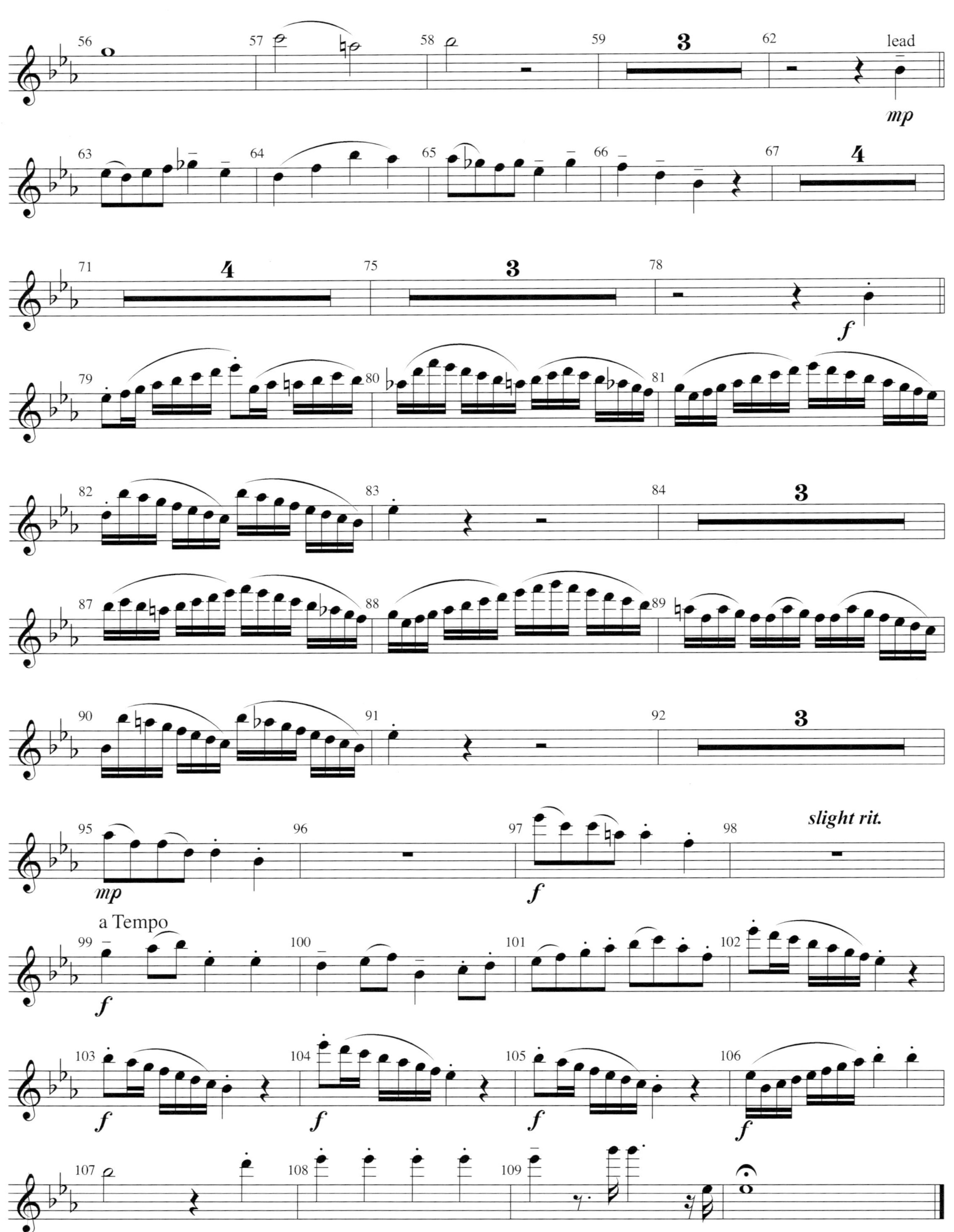
CHAMPAGNE VARIATIONS pg. 2

lead
mp
mp
lead
mp
lead
mf
not lead
mp
p
p
p
CHAMPAGNE VARIATIONS pg. 5

CHAMPAGNE VARIATIONS pg. 6

CHAMPAGNE VARIATIONS pg. 7